The Belcher Book

Written by Sean Watermeyer

Illustrated by Vanessa Williams

Belchers and Burpers are everywhere,
whether you are big or small.

It does not matter how old you are,
or if you are ten foot tall.

There is a Burper in every house,
up and down the land.

Even Granny does a
naughty burp,
although it's never
planned!

Baby Beth needs to burp after she's had her milk.

Smelly ones...

And LOUD
ones!...

But some as soft as
silk.

She turns all red and strains...

Then belches to her hearts galore...

Then a smile appears upon her face,
her tummy's no longer sore.

Toddler Tim likes a burp,
when he's had his grub.

And when he can't expel the wind,
his tummy needs a rub.

When Dad is eating fish and chips,
sitting in front of the telly.

You know when he is going to burp,
cos' of the rumblings in his belly.

Mum too, can get very cross,
when Dad's had a beer or three.

He wants a cuddle, then a snuggle
and his bottom burps go free.

"Excuse me please!?"
says Mum,
when from your drink you slurp.

But ***WOW*** how cross she really gets,
when you smile and have a burp.

But Grandad is the worst,
he trumpets from both ends.

Mummy says that is why, he doesn't
have any friends.

I think burping is funny,
it always gets a giggle.

And when you are on the dance floor,
you can do it with a wiggle.

Our next door neighbour made
his living,
dear old Mr Brian Welcher.

He made a thousand,
no a million,
from being a World
Championship Belcher.

BEST
BELCH

When he was young and ambitious,
he could belch the alphabet.

And all his school pals used to say,
that is why he was the teacher's pet.

Bottom burps do happen,
but they are mainly from the top.

Especially when you have guzzled down,
that bottle of fizzy pop.

So burps come loud and soft,
they can be whiffy or sweet.

But oh what a relief to release that burp,
it really is a treat.

Printed in Great Britain
by Amazon